MY FRIEND

AMY

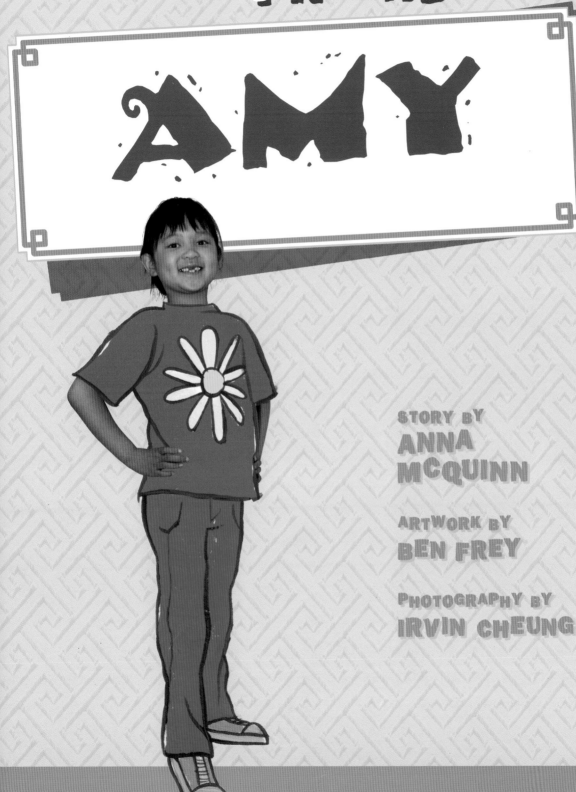

STORY BY
ANNA
MCQUINN

ARTWORK BY
BEN FREY

PHOTOGRAPHY BY
IRVIN CHEUNG

ALANNA BOOKS

My friend is Chinese.
Well, actually, she was
born here, just like me.

The first day at my new school,
the teacher sat me next to her.
She was really friendly and played with me
at break and we've been friends ever since.
My name is Monifa, her name is Amy.

We're in Year 3 now, and we still sit next to each other. Our favourite subject is art.

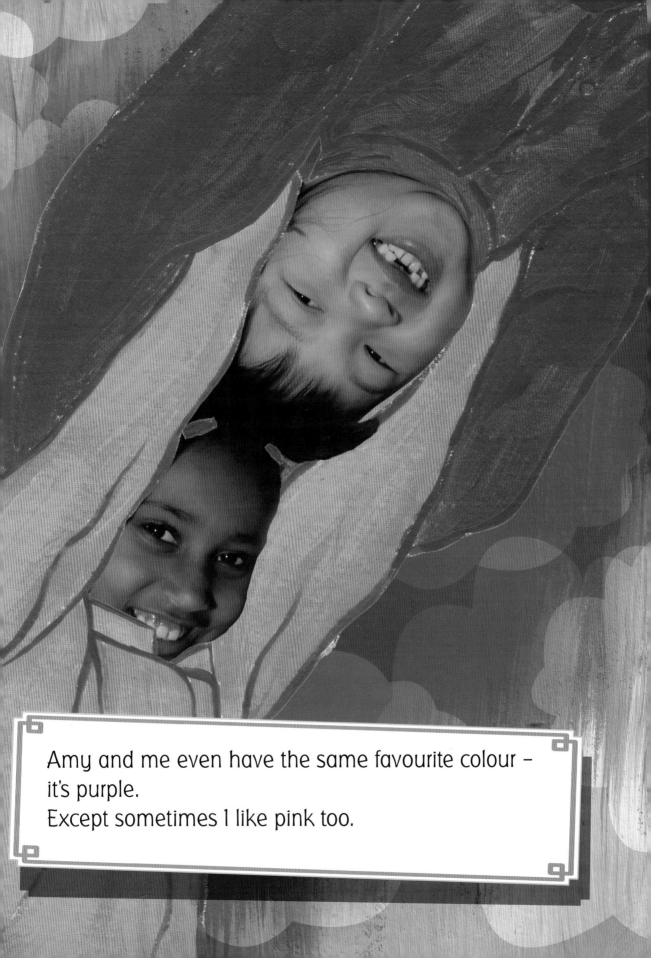

Amy and me even have the same favourite colour – it's purple.
Except sometimes I like pink too.

At Amy's house, we mostly do loads of drawing.
I have glitter pens and markers,
and she has gel pens and felt tips.

Sometimes we make a bit of a mess. Luckily Amy's grandma is there a lot. She doesn't ever tell us off – as long as we do our homework first, she's happy.

Amy calls her grandma *Por Por* – that's Chinese.
Amy's grandma calls Amy *Mei Jing* – that's her real
Chinese name. *Mei* means 'beautiful' and *Jing* means
'sparkling crystal'. I think it's so cool to have two names.

馬家果店

My name means 'I am lucky' in Yoruba,
which is a language they speak in West Africa.
Amy's grandma says it's the best name ever.

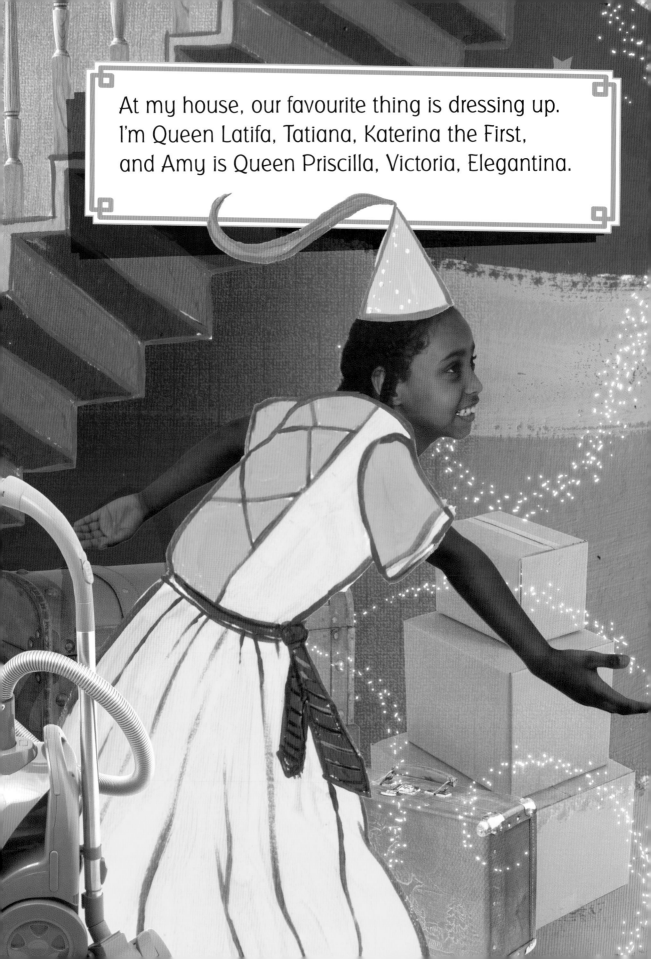

At my house, our favourite thing is dressing up.
I'm Queen Latifa, Tatiana, Katerina the First,
and Amy is Queen Priscilla, Victoria, Elegantina.

We have a secret chamber under the stairs
and a throne and a big book all about our kingdom.

One day I went with Amy to her grandma's house.
It was full of Amy's aunts and cousins.

I thought it must be someone's birthday,
but Amy says her whole family gets together all the time.
I learned how to use chopsticks – that was wicked!
It's actually not even hard.

Amy's grandma cooked heaps of food.
I liked the fish balls best. They were kind of spongy –
tasty and weird at the same time.
Amy said if I thought they were weird I was lucky
her grandma hadn't cooked chicken's feet!

My nana cooks weird stuff too. Her favourite thing from when she was a little girl is cow's foot. *Eeuu!*

When Amy's grandma was little, her family
were farmers in Hong Kong.
But life got very hard so they came to England.

They started a restaurant and had to work really really hard. Amy's grandma had to help out, even though she was only six. Amy's grandma says you have to work hard to start a new life.

In March, Amy got a new dog. He's so cute. We decided to call him Charlie because he has such a cheeky face.

We take Charlie for walks in the park. Sometimes, Amy lets me hold the lead. That's just brilliant.

When we're big, Amy and me are going to be animal doctors and open a huge clinic. Animals can come if they are sick or just if they need a hug.

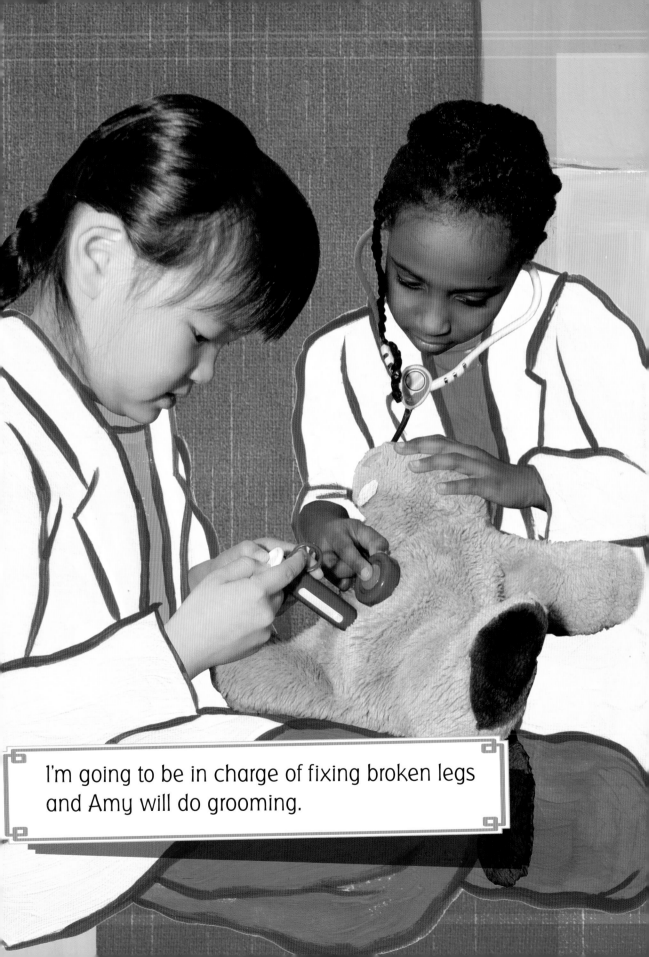

I'm going to be in charge of fixing broken legs and Amy will do grooming.

Amy and I go to Drama Club on Tuesdays.
For Chinese New Year, we all learned two new dances.

We did them in a show at the community centre.
First the Dragon Dance, then the Fan Dance.
We got to wear two cool costumes and everyone
cheered. It was brilliant.

After, Amy's parents gave Amy and me red envelopes.
We made red envelopes for Chinese New Year in school,
but they only had chocolate money inside.
Amy's family put in real money!

Amy says she gets them on her birthday and when she gets good marks, so I bet she will be rich soon. I think our school should do a note to parents and have real money next Chinese New Year.

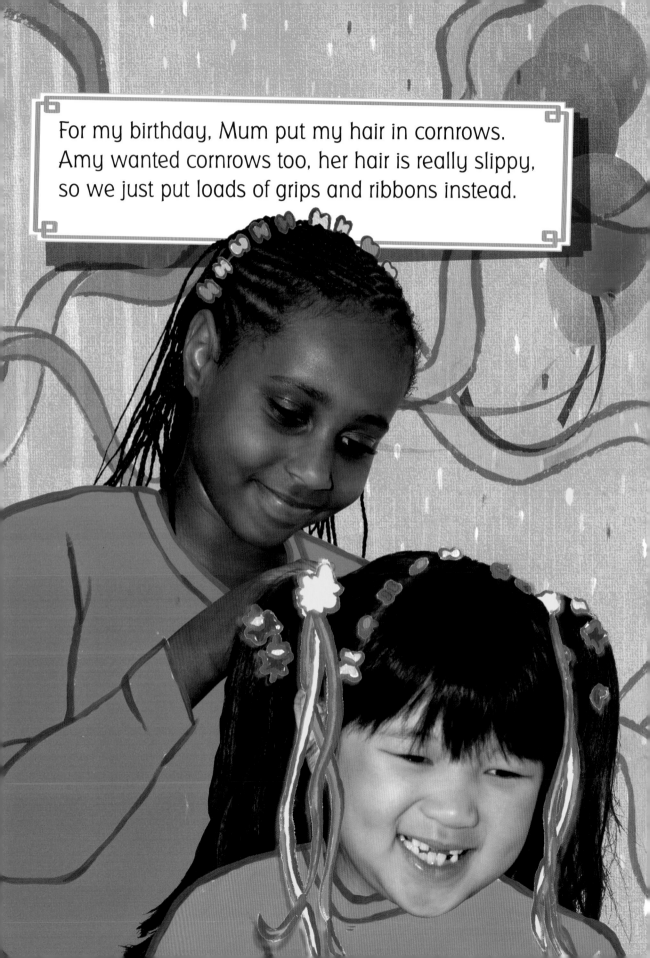

For my birthday, Mum put my hair in cornrows. Amy wanted cornrows too, her hair is really slippy, so we just put loads of grips and ribbons instead.

Amy gave me a brilliant charm bracelet —
it has flowers inside glass beads and hearts
and butterflies and a little Chinese coin.

Then, we played Explorers.
We discovered a new country
and made up our own language.

We pretended our marshmallows were a new kind of fruit and then we ate them all.
For my birthday, Amy let me eat most of the pink ones.

On Saturdays, we like go to the playground.
Amy can get higher than me on the swings,
but mostly we try to be equals.
That's because we're best friends.

Thanks to Sho Ying and Amy for answering all my questions – and for the interesting chats, and to Katie, Isabel, Sebastian and Isabella for being inspiring.

This book is dedicated to My Friends Margaret, Jana, Marijn and Susanna who all know how to really listen... AMQ

The photographer would like to thank Victoria Cheung and Martha Asfaw and their families for their invaluable contribution.

Main photos (Monifa, Amy, and family) by Irvin Cheung. Artwork by Ben Frey.
Additional photography credits: playground: © istockphoto.com/Rami Ben Ami; single house: © istockphoto.com/ Jim Pruitt; row of houses: © istockphoto.com/Oktay Ortakcioglu; deciduous tree: © istockphoto.com/ Christine Balderas; coniferous tree: © istockphoto.com/Olga Zinatova; pottery tools: ©istockphoto.com/Jason Lugo; lump of clay © Irvin Cheung; vase: © istockphoto.com/Coral Coolahan; dresser: © istockphoto.com; potted plant: © istockphoto.com/Eliza Snow; bok choy, choy sum cordyceps fungi: © istockphoto.com/Norman Chan; lychee: © istockphoto.com/John Peacock; durian: © istockphoto. com/Fadhil Kamarudin; red Chinese lanterns: © istockphoto.com/Frank van den Bergh; hanging lamps: © Irvin Cheung; lantern fruit and cinnamon sticks: © istockphoto.com/Junghee Choi; stair railing: ©istockphoto.com/Nina Shannon; vacuum cleaner: © istockphoto.com/Emrah Turudu; leather trunk: © istockphoto.com/Les Palenik; suitcase: © istockphoto.com; cardboard boxes: © istockphoto.com/Carlos Alvarez; castle: © istockphoto.com; butterfly (right and left): © istockphoto.com/Cathy Keifer; butterfly (center) © istockphoto.com/Goran Kapor; brick houses: © istockphoto.com/Owen Price; flower pattern texture: © istockphoto.com/senkonate; plates of food: © Irvin Cheung; chicken's foot: © istockphoto.com/Sawayasu Tsuji; cow's hoof: © istockphoto.com/Jorge Gonzalez; Hong Kong ferry: © istockphoto.com/Tan Kian Khoon; Hong Kong tram: © Christine Gonslaves/Dreamstime.com; Jade Palace restaurant, Calgary, Alberta: Glenbow Archives NA-2645-53; family portrait, restaurant interior: Courtesy of Ken Chow; photo album: © istockphoto.com; envelope: © istockphoto.com/Anja Hild; wood texture: © istockphoto.com/Bill Noll; Jack Russell terrier: © istockphoto.com/Claudio Arnese; pagoda and trees: © istockphoto. com; picture frame: © istockphoto.com/Csaba Zsarnowszky; clock: © istockphoto.com; thermometer: © istockphoto.com/ Eugene Berman; bandaids: © istockphoto.com/Yunus Arakon; black dart and blue dart: © istockphoto.com; red dart: © istockphoto.com/Boris Yankov; green pennant: © istockphoto.com/Stefan Klein; red checkered pennant: © istockphoto.com/ Valerie Loiseleux; chest of coins: © istockphoto.com/Ivan Mateev; diamonds: © istockphoto.com/Evgeny Terentyev; pile of gold coins: © istockphoto.com/Elnur Amikishiyev; stack of bills and piggy banks: © istockphoto.com/ Ivana Starcevic; balloons: © istockphoto.com; glass heart: © istockphoto.com/Liudmila Otrutskaya; cloisonne eggs: © istockphoto.com/Hector Joseph Lumang; blue glass bead and butterfly bead: © istockphoto.com; Chinese coin: © istockphoto.com/Hector Joseph Lumang; clothes peg: © istockphoto.com/Patricia Nelson; African blanket pattern: © istockphoto.com/Peeter Viisimaa; kerosene lantern: © istockphoto.com/Juan Monino; Calgary skyline: © istockphoto.com; gerbera daisies: © istockphoto.com/Kais Tolmats

First published in the United Kingdom in 2009
by Alanna Books
46 Chalvey Road East, Slough, Berkshire,
SL1 2LR, United Kingdom

© 2009 Anna McQuinn (text)
© 2008 Ben Frey (artwork)
First published in 2009 by Annick Press, Canada
Cover and interior design by Irvin Cheung / iCheung Design

All rights reserved. No part of this work covered by the copyrights hereon may be reproduced or used in any form or by any means—graphic, electronic, or mechanical—without prior written permission of the publisher.

www.alanna.demon.co.uk

ISBN: 978-0-9551998-3-7

Printed and bound in China